SEE INSIDE BACK COVER

£3.10

Printed and Published in Great Britain by D. C. THOMSON & CO.,
LTD., 185 Fleet Street, London EC4A 2HS. © D. C. THOMSON &
CO., LTD., 1988.
ISBN   0-85116-412-9

£2.49

ROGER'S DODGE CLINIC

Dear Roger,
How do we dodge eating Olive's ghastly school dinners? Yours disgustedly,
The Bash Street Kids

THE FIRST THING TO DO IS ASK FOR MORE.

WH-WHAT?

MORE JELLY PLEASE, OLIVE.

OLIVE

CERTAINLY, DANNY — HAVE A VAT.

OLIVE

NOW YOU CAN MAKE SOME MONEY.

TRAMPOLINE FOR HIRE 10p A TURN

YOU KNOW WHAT TO DO WITH THIS MONEY . . .

FLIP

. . . BUY SOME DELICIOUS JUNK FOOD — MUCH HEALTHIER THAN OLIVE'S!

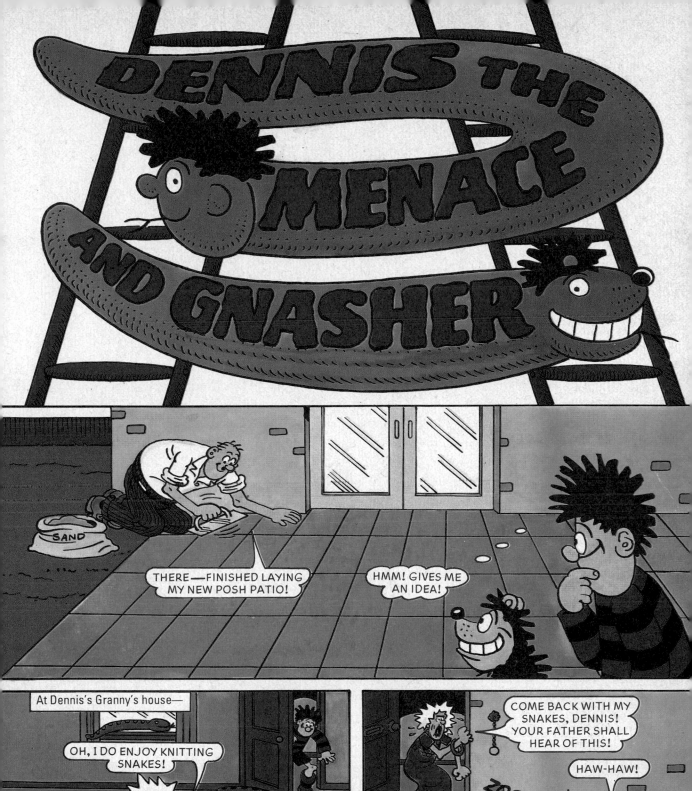

DENNIS THE MENACE AND GNASHER

THERE—FINISHED LAYING MY NEW POSH PATIO!

HMM! GIVES ME AN IDEA!

At Dennis's Granny's house—

OH, I DO ENJOY KNITTING SNAKES!

DRAUGHT EXCLUDER

TIP TOE

CLICK! CLICK!

COME BACK WITH MY SNAKES, DENNIS! YOUR FATHER SHALL HEAR OF THIS!

HAW-HAW!

ZOOM!

At the Circus—

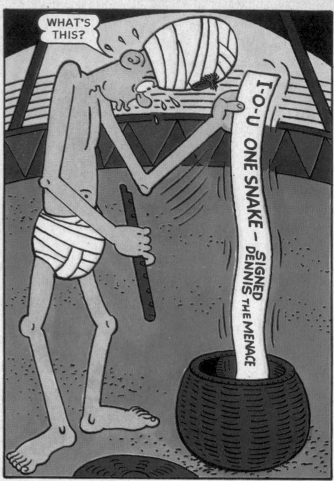

ROGER'S DODGE CLINIC

Dear Roger,

How do I keep Rasher out of my turnip patch?

Yours worriedly,
Dennis's Dad

THE BEST THING IS TO MAKE A BIG, UGLY TURNIP LANTERN.

CAN'T SEE THE POINT OF THIS.

THEN LIGHT IT.

CHOMP! GUZZLE! GULP!

KNEW IT WOULDN'T WORK — HE STILL ATE IT.

BUT HE WON'T EAT MUCH MORE TODAY.

OINKGASP! THAT GAVE ME TERRIBLE HEARTBURN.

The WINTER OLYMPIGS

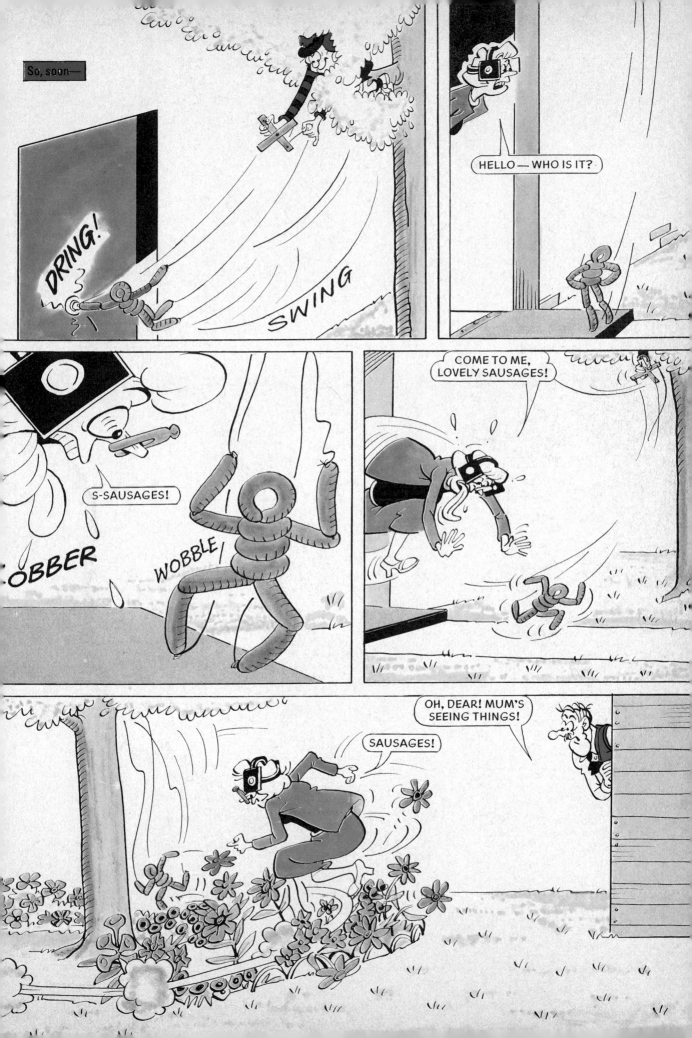

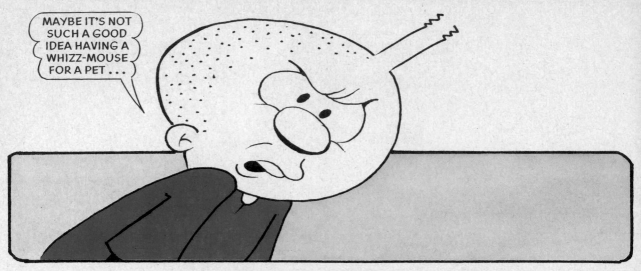

PUP PARADE

PICTURE ① Pups laying around bin.
Pug – "What'll we do today, Pups?"

Tubby at open letter-box.
"Don't know! The "Beano" Editor hasn't sent us
our story script to follow today!"

PICTURE ②

What'll we do today, Pups?

PUG →
PEEPS
WIGGY
BONES
VERY SILLY SNIFFY
TUBBY
'ENRY
SPOTTY
MANFRID

Don't know! The "Beano" Editor hasn't sent us our story script to follow today!

PUPS' LETTERS

I know – we'll write our own script for the artist to draw!

The Pups find...

ROGER'S DODGE CLINIC

Dear Roger,
I am very bothered by toothache — Gnipper's tooth makes me ache quite a lot!
Yours painfully,
Dennis's Postie

WHAT YOU NEED IS A CORK FOR HIS TOOTH.

THIS ONE WILL DO.

POP!

PLOP!

NA-NA-NA-NA-NOW YOU CAN'T BITE ME!

GRR! MY LEMONADE'S GONE FLAT WITHOUT THE CORK.

So—

GRAB

TWANG!

CHOMP!

THAT DODGE DOESN'T WORK AGAINST ALL KINDS OF TEETH.

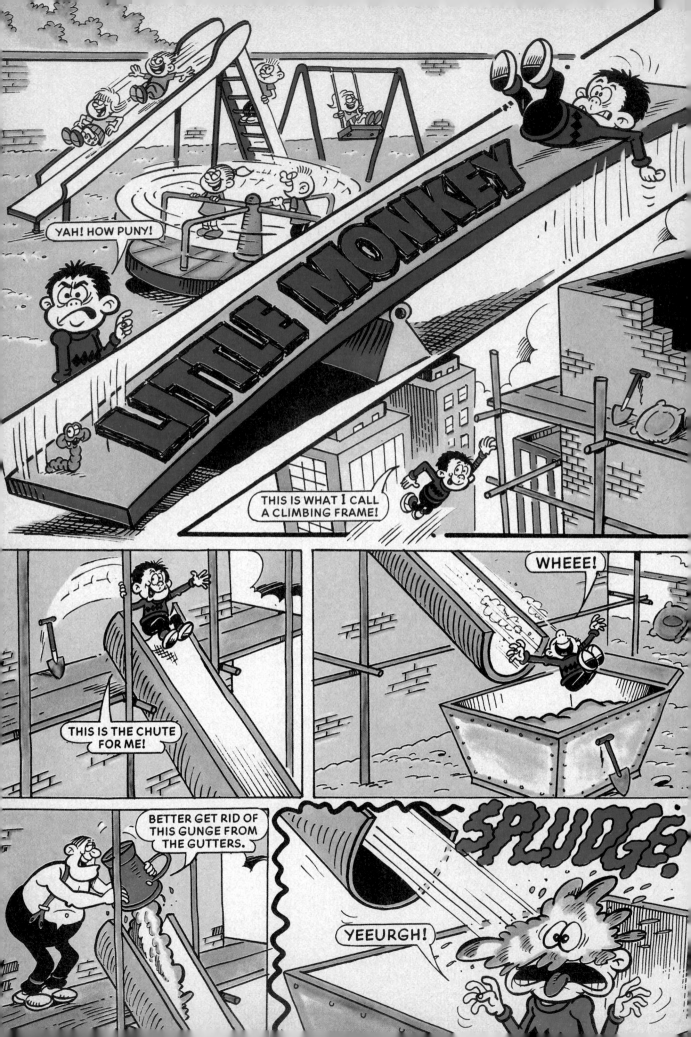

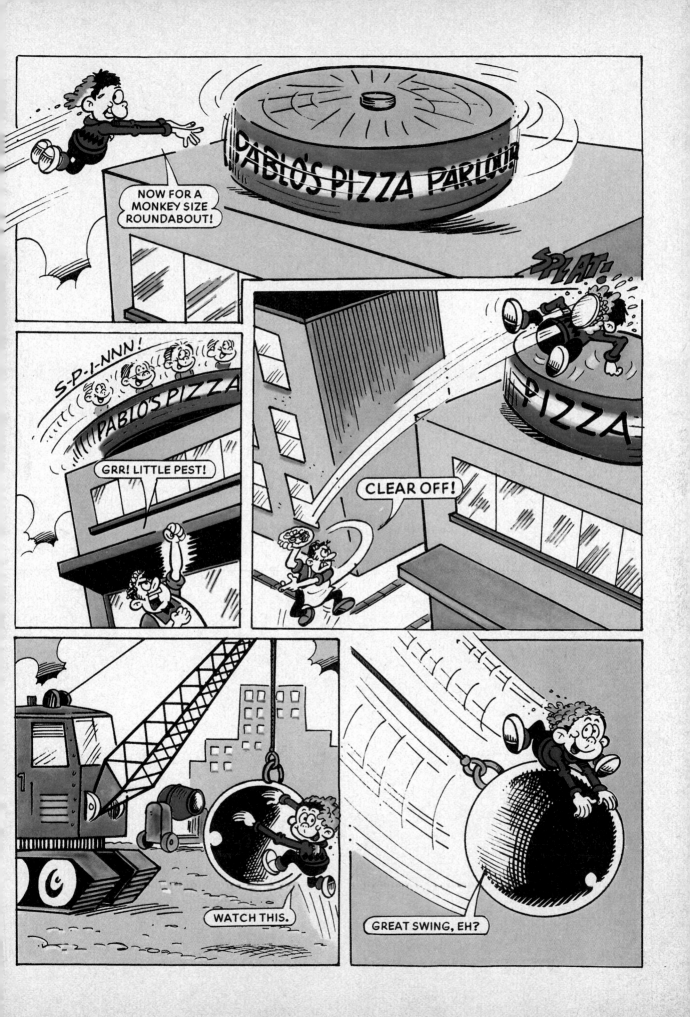

MONKEY PUZZLES

How many bananas are in this picture?

Wrong! There are sixteen!

Can you make a monkey out of these?

Simple, eh?

Pin the tail on the monkey—
Put on a blindfold and try it!

(Copy the tail on to card.)

KARATE SID

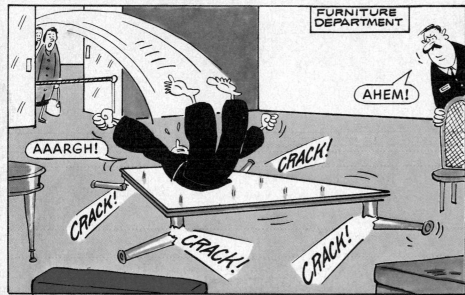

So—

TWO OF THE TOUGHEST GIRLS IN "THE BEANO" PLAYING WITH A PRAM? I DON'T BELIEVE IT!

LET'S SEE YOUR DOLLY, MY PRETTY MAIDS! SNIGGER!

YOU'LL BE SORRY!

WAH!

ITCHING POWDER

TOLD YOU YOU'D BE SORRY!

TH-THERE GO TOOTS, MINNIE AND IVY!

Meanwhile—

CALAMITY JAMES →

I'VE BEEN REALLY LUCKY TODAY! I'VE ONLY MISSED BREAKFAST, LOST MY POCKET-MONEY, STOOD IN . . .

ALEXANDER LEMMING

VROOOM!

. . . I'M SURE I SAW CALAMITY JAMES JUST NOW.

I WAS SURE, TOO! WHERE'D HE GO?

SPLURP!

. . . BEEN RUN OVER BY A PRAM, DROPPED ON BY A PARACHUTIST, CAUGHT BY THE . . .

I'M NEARLY ON A DIET, FOLKS — I HAVEN'T EATEN A THING SINCE BREAKFAST!

ONE WILLING VOLUNTEER COMING UP!

YIKES!

WELL, WHAT DO YOU THINK OF OUR COOKING, JOE?

GROOGH! I'LL NEVER EAT AGAIN — NOT TILL LUNCHTIME ANYWAY!

AW, WHAT A SHAME! HE DIDN'T LIKE IT! GIGGLE!

GIRLS LIKE PLAYING WITH SKIPPING ROPES, TOO!

AND WE'VE GOT AN EXTRA-LONG ROPE...

SKIP! SKIP!

...LET'S TAKE IT TO THE FOOTBALL PITCH!

So—

EEK!

GRR! YOU SPOILED OUR GAME!

WELL, YOU SPOILED OUR SKIPPING! HAW-HAW-HAW!

ROGER'S DODGE CLINIC

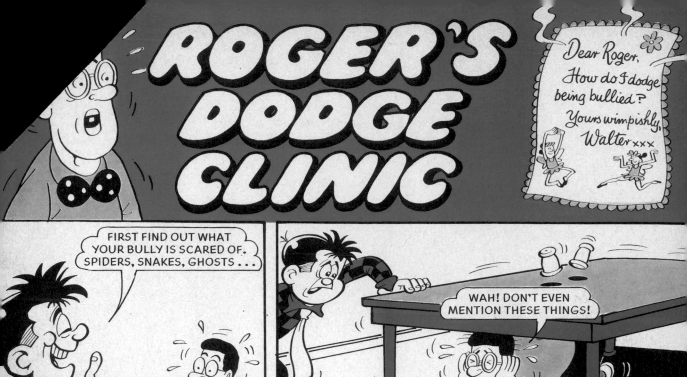

FIRST FIND OUT WHAT YOUR BULLY IS SCARED OF. SPIDERS, SNAKES, GHOSTS . . .

WAH! DON'T EVEN MENTION THESE THINGS!

/TREMBLE/

YOU'LL JUST HAVE TO HIRE A BODYGUARD.

I'LL DO THE JOB FOR AN EGG FOO YUCK SPECIAL.

WHO'S BULLYING YOU THEN, DENNIS THE MENACE, MINNIE THE MINX?

NO — MY NAUGHTY TEDDY — HE WON'T LET ME HAVE ENOUGH SPACE IN BED.

RRIP!

SLAP!

I WARNED YOU, YOU GREAT PUDDING!

HERE'S TODAY'S PARTY LINE UP — BALL BOY, BENJY, TITCH AND DIMMY.

WE'LL HAVE A TEAM GAME, BALL BOY — PASSING THE BALLOON TO EACH OTHER FROM UNDER YOUR CHIN.

WE WIN!

WOW! HOW ARE YOU SO GOOD?

IT'S OUR LATEST TACTIC ON THE FOOTBALL FIELD!

PYOING!

WHY DO I AGREE TO THIS EVERY YEAR?

BECAUSE WE ALWAYS BRING YOU A CHRISTMAS PRESENT.

OH, YES — THAT'S THE REASON.

BIG E

THE THINGS PEOPLE WILL DO FOR A "DENNIS THE MENACE" BOOK!

DENNIS the MENACE 1989

I'M GOING TO RE-DECORATE MY ROOM.

TIDDLES IS SCRAPING OFF THE OLD WALLPAPER...

RIP!

...GRANNY'S MIXING THE PASTE...

...AND FRANKIE'S DOING THE HANGING.

ROGER'S DODGE CLINIC

Dear Roger

How do I dodge bad luck?

Yours unfortunately,
Calamity James

GNASHER in DAD'S ARMY

ZOOM!

READER'S VOICE
LOOK OUT, GNASHER— YOU'RE GOING TO BE HIT BY SNOWBALLS.

NOT SNOWBALLS — IT'S GNAOMI, GNATASHA, GNORAH, GNANCY AND GNANETTE— MY GIRLS.

ZOOM!

BATH TIME, GNASHER!

WHERE IS GNASHER? ALL I CAN SEE IS A SHEEP.

THAT'S ODD! A SHEEP?

FOR YOU, DEAREST DAD.

DOGGY NEWS

IT'S VERY HANDY HAVING ALL THESE DAUGHTERS.

PAGE 3
DOGGY NEWS

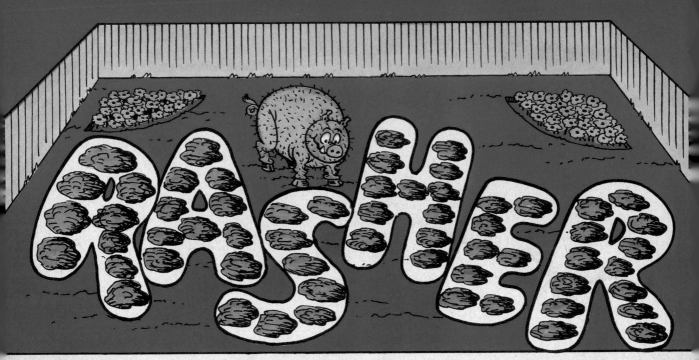

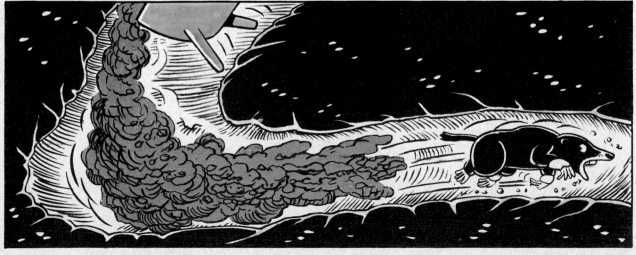

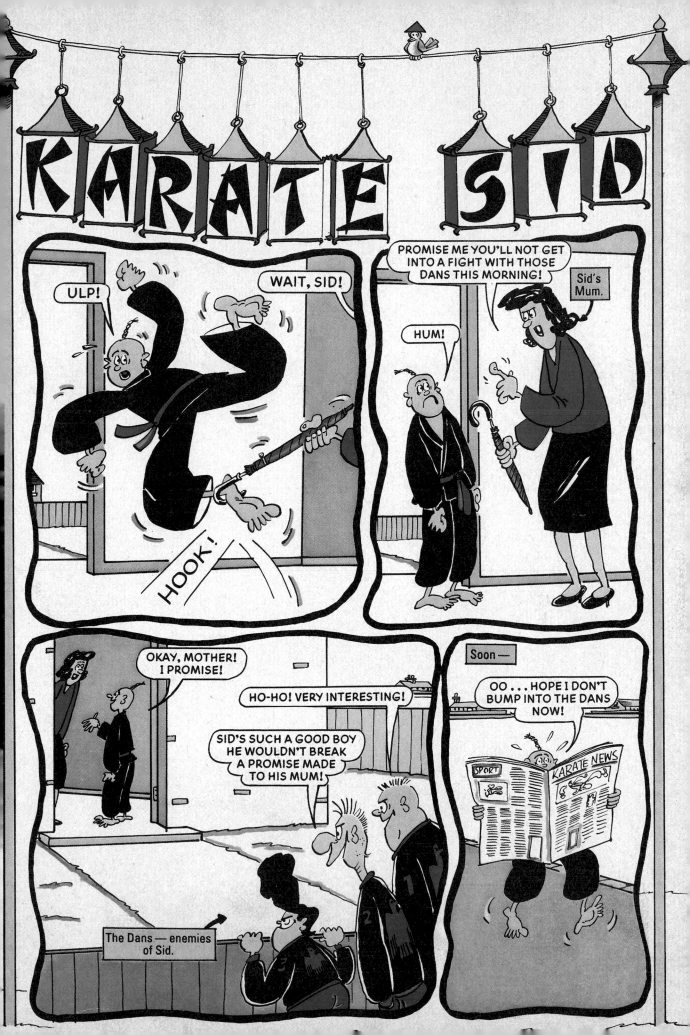

LITTLE PLUM and

"BABYFACE"

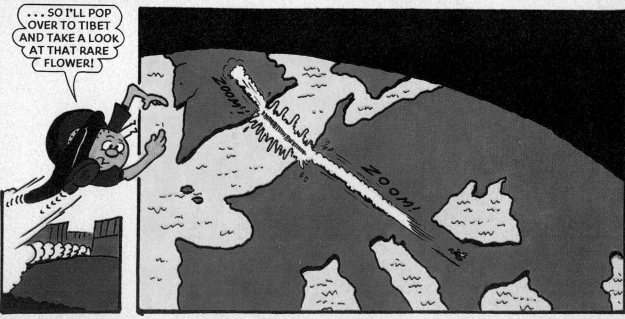

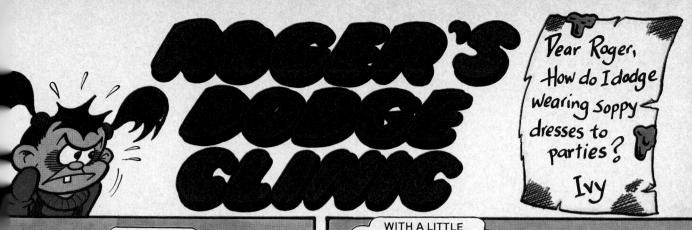

Biffo the Bear

OLD FRIEND BIFFO HAD A BATH.
EE-AY-EE-AY-O!

AND IN THAT BATH
HE HAD A DUCK.
EE-AY-EE-AY-O!

WITH A QUACK-QUACK
HERE AND A QUACK-QUACK
THERE, HERE A QUACK, THERE
A QUACK, EVERYWHERE
A QUACK-QUACK . . .

. . . OLD FRIEND
BIFFO HAD A BATH.
EE-AY-EE-AY-O!